choose to love
A Poem about life, love and choices

poem composed by c. kevin wanzer

artwork created by kristin tuller

first published by AuthorHouse february 14, 2006

ISBN: 1-4208-9521-4 (sc)

printed in Canada

this book is printed on acid-free paper

authorHOUSE

1663 liberty drive
bloomington, indiana 47403
(800) 839-8640
www.authorhouse.com

abby ◆ adam ◆ alisha ◆ alice ◆ allison ◆ angela ◆ angelina ◆ angie ◆ anna ◆ amy ◆ arthur ◆ barbara ◆ barney ◆ becky ◆ beebo ◆ benjamin ◆ betsy ◆ betty ◆ bill ◆ bob ◆ bobby ◆ boy ◆ brad ◆ brady ◆ brandi ◆ brian ◆ brooke ◆ bryan ◆ brent ◆ brett ◆ bud ◆ carlie ◆ carolyn ◆ casey ◆ chad ◆ chris ◆ christine ◆ cindy ◆ c and a j ◆ cletus ◆ coleen ◆ connie ◆ corey ◆ corin ◆ corwin ◆ corky ◆ courtney ◆ craig ◆ dad ◆ daniel ◆ danielle ◆ danny ◆ dashiell ◆ david ◆ debbie ◆ des ◆ dharma ◆ didier ◆ don ◆ doug ◆ dreifus ◆ dudley ◆ ed ◆ eli ◆ ellen ◆ eloise ◆ eric ◆ gerri ◆ glenn ◆ gloria ◆ erin ◆ franklin ◆ grandma ◆ grandpa ◆ gray ◆ hannah ◆ harold ◆ hazyl ◆ henry ◆ hilary

**dedicated to
brandon & christopher**

**& to all of those who help me
choose to love**

holly ◆ ingrid ◆ jack ◆ jackson ◆ jake ◆ jane ◆ jason ◆ jeanne ◆ jeff ◆ jennifer ◆ jeri ◆ jerry ◆ jill ◆ jim ◆ john ◆ jolene ◆ jon ◆ juan ◆ judy ◆ julia ◆ julie ◆ justin ◆ kalen ◆ kara ◆ karen ◆ karl ◆ kathy ◆ katie ◆ kenny ◆ kent ◆ kevin ◆ kim ◆ kristin ◆ kristy ◆ lauren ◆ leah ◆ lena ◆ linda ◆ lilly ◆ lori ◆ lorie lee ◆ lucky ◆ lucy ◆ luke ◆ lynn ◆ mae ◆ maddy ◆ maisie ◆ maria ◆ martha ◆ mary ◆ mary ann ◆ mark ◆ matt ◆ mattie ◆ maya ◆ meg ◆ melanie ◆ michael ◆ michelle ◆ mike ◆ minnieta ◆ mom ◆ nanny ◆ nigel ◆ oprah ◆ pam ◆ patrick ◆ patty ◆ paul ◆ pete ◆ phil ◆ ray ◆ richard ◆ rick ◆ rj ◆ rob ◆ roc ◆ roxie ◆ ryan ◆ sara ◆ sam ◆ scott ◆ squishy ◆ steve ◆ sue ◆ susan ◆ suzanne ◆ tad ◆ tbayt ◆ terry ◆ tom ◆ trent ◆ tru ◆ ty ◆ vicki ◆ vijay ◆ vince ◆ vivian ◆ whit ◆ will da will it is amazing in this world today

filled with love and hate

what separates the common one,

from the one who is truly great

for it's not the wealth

in your bank account

or the possessions

in your own back yard

it is instead,

what you share from inside

of your loving,

compassionate heart

you do not choose
your color of skin,
you don't choose
to be born rich or poor

you do not choose

to be deaf or blind,

wishing you had something more

Introducing custom-blend
when you want to wear it,
you'll love. You can even bu

you do not choose

with whom you fall in love,

you don`t choose

to be born woman or man

you do not choose

your family,

it's all part of God's great plan

and although for some,

it's hard to relate

to the differences others endure,

keep in mind there are certain choices

that make you shallow or pure

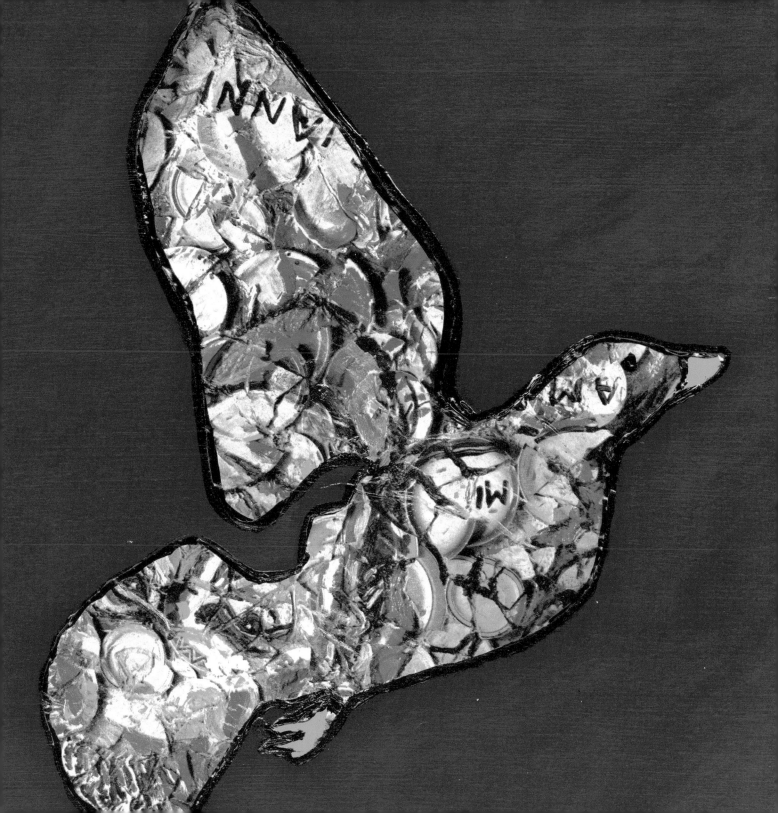

you do

choose to love

or hate

you do
choose to follow
or lead

you do choose

to embrace or ignore,

others in their time of need

some things in life,

you cannot alter

but your attitude can change,
it`s true

and by doing so,

you can affect

the people who look up to you

the meaning of life

is the greatest mystery of all

but the answer is easily found

it is unconditional love

for ALL humankind

who walk on our common ground

c. kevin wanzer, author

is an honors graduate of Butler University, was born in Chicago and raised in Indianapolis, Indiana.

Since his sophomore year in high school, Kevin has been reaching countless audiences of all ages around the world, as he shares his message of love, leadership and laughter.

Kevin has worked as an intern for the David Letterman Show, presented at the United Nations and was appointed to the White House Conference for a Drug Free America.

Kevin is blessed to share his life in Indianapolis with his family Brandon, Christopher, Maisie and Mattie.

kristin tuller, illustrator

is a graduate of Indiana University and was born and raised in Indianapolis, Indiana. Kristin has been fulfilling her dream of being an artist, professionally, since 1995.

When she is not painting, Kristin spends her time waiting tables, reading, writing and running. She has spent countless years working with both children and adults who have special needs. Currently, she's pursuing a masters degree in art therapy from Indiana University.

Friends with Kevin since childhood, she too makes her home in Indianapolis.

choose to love products & speaking information
www.ChooseToLove.com ~ www.KevinWanzer.com